Big Barry Baker
in big trouble

Written by Gill and Paul Hamlyn

Illustrated by Philippe Dupasquier

Heinemann

Chapter 1

One day Big Barry Baker and his three
friends, Josie, Liz and Roy, were in the
school playground. They started to talk
about their mums and dads.

'My dad's a postman,' said Liz. 'He carries lots of letters in his bag.'

'My mum's a teacher,' said Roy. 'She works in the big school down the road.'

'My dad's a painter,' said Josie. 'He has a big van with a ladder on the roof.'

'That's nothing,' said Barry. 'My mum's
a policewoman. She has to go out every
night and catch burglars.'
'No she isn't,' said Josie, Liz and Roy.
'We don't believe you.'

Big Barry Baker started to get cross.

'My mum **is** a policewoman,' he said.

'And my dad **is** a fireman.'

'And I bet your brother is an ambulance
driver!' said Liz.

Josie and Roy started to laugh.

That made Big Barry Baker very cross.

He pushed his friends out of the way
and walked off.

Big Barry Baker sat alone. He could see
all his friends talking about him and
laughing. He wanted to cry but he didn't.

Chapter 2

In the classroom Mr Wise said,
'Today we are going to find out about
people who help us. Can you think of
someone who helps us?'
The children put up their hands.

'The police help us,' said Liz.
'Yes, they do,' said Mr Wise. 'Can you
tell me how the police help us?'
The children put up their hands again.

'They stop cars
from going
too fast,' said Josie.

'They help us to cross
the road,' said Roy.

'And they catch
burglars,' said Liz.

Suddenly Big Barry Baker jumped up.
'My mum is a policewoman,' he said.
All the children turned round and
looked at him.
'No she isn't,' they called out.
'Sit down, Barry,' said Mr Wise.
So Big Barry Baker sat down.

'Now,' said Mr Wise. 'Can you think of
other people who help us?'
Roy put up his hand.
'Firemen help us,' he said.
'Yes, they do,' said Mr Wise. 'Can you
tell me how firemen help us?'
The children put up their hands.
'They put out fires,' said Josie.

Once again, Big Barry Baker jumped up.
'My dad is a fireman,' he said.
All the children turned round and
looked at him.
'No he isn't,' they called out.
'Sit down, Barry,' said Mr Wise.
So Big Barry Baker sat down.

11

But Big Barry Baker was not going to
give up, so he put up his hand.
'Yes, Barry?' said Mr Wise.
'My mum **is** a policewoman,' said Barry.
'If the school burglar alarm went off,
she would come to school in her police car
and help us.'

The other children started to laugh,
but Big Barry Baker went on,
'And my dad **is** a fireman. If the school
fire alarm went off, he would come
to school in his fire engine and help us.'
The other children in the class laughed
even louder.
Big Barry Baker's face went very red.

'Thank you, Barry,' said Mr Wise.

'Now be quiet everyone.'

Big Barry Baker was very cross.

He could tell that no one believed him.

'I'll show them,' he said to himself.

Chapter 3

At play time all the children went out
into the playground.
Josie, Liz and Roy couldn't see
Big Barry Baker anywhere.
'I wonder where Barry is?' said Roy.

They were just about to start looking
for him when suddenly the school alarm
bells went off. Everyone could hear the
alarms all over the school.

The school alarms set off an alarm in the police station.

As soon as the alarm went off, a police car left the station and came quickly down the road to the school.

The school alarms set off an alarm in
the fire station too.

As soon as the alarm went off, a fire
engine left the station and came quickly
down the road to the school.

By now all the teachers and children were out in the playground.

Big Barry Baker ran across to them with a little smile on his face.

'There you are, Barry,' said Josie, Liz and Roy. 'Where have you been?'

'Nowhere,' said Big Barry Baker.

...n, the police car pulled up
...the school and out jumped
a policewoman.

'Look,' said the children. 'It's Big Barry
Baker's mum! She **is** a policewoman.'

Then the fire engine pulled up outside the school and out jumped a fireman. 'Look,' said the children. 'It's Big Barry Baker's dad! He **is** a fireman.'

Big Barry Baker's mum and dad ran into the school. Soon they came out again and went over to talk to Mr Wise. They looked very cross.

'Barry Baker!' shouted Mr Wise.

'Will you come over here now, please?'

Big Barry Baker was in BIG TROUBLE.

'Did you set off the alarms, Barry?'
asked Mr Wise.

'Yes,' said Big Barry Baker. 'I'm sorry.
I just wanted to show everyone that
my mum is a policewoman, and my dad
is a fireman. No one would believe me!'

'Well they do now,' said his mum and
dad. 'But you must never do anything
like that again!'

That day Big Barry Baker's friends couldn't wait to get home from school. They wanted to tell everyone that Big Barry Baker's mum was a policewoman and his dad was a fireman. And no one was ever going to forget it!